Disclaimer

Every effort has been made to ensure that the information contained within this guide is accurate at the time of publication. How2Become Ltd is not responsible for anyone failing any part of any selection process as a result of the information contained within this guide. How2Become Ltd and their authors cannot accept any responsibility for any errors or omissions within this guide, however caused. No responsibility for loss or damage occasioned by any person acting, or refraining from action, as a result of the material in this publication can be accepted by How2Become Ltd.

The information within this guide does not represent the views of any third-party service or organisation.

GW00656647

how2become

QUICK-FIRE MATHS POCKETBOOK

*SECRETS AND TRICKS TO INCREASE
YOUR MATHEMATICAL SPEED*

www.How2Become.com

Orders: Please contact How2Become Ltd, Suite 14, 50 Churchill Square Business Centre, Kings Hill, Kent ME19 4YU.

You can order through Amazon.co.uk under ISBN **9781912370177**, via the website www.How2Become.com, Gardners or Bertrams.

ISBN: **9781912370177**

First published in 2018 by How2Become Ltd.

Typeset for How2Become Ltd by Katie Noakes.

Contents

MULTIPLICATION 31

INTRODUCTION

Welcome to the mathematical world of tips and tricks! This Rapid Maths Pocketbook will guide you through some of the most basic mathematical calculations; bringing your attention to some of the best tips and tricks you can apply to your learning.

With the help of our neat little tricks, and a different perspective into the world of mathematics, you too will be able to master the basics with regards to simple multiplication, division, addition, and subtraction calculations.

One of the best things you will gain from this book is the ability to work quickly through a mathematical problem. Whether you are trying to work out the total discount of your purchase, or trying to split the bill in a restaurant; our book will allow you to practice the key skills and techniques to work out all of this!

How Will This Book Benefit Me?

Not only will you learn an array of techniques that will benefit your mathematical learning, but you will also be able to learn NEW ways of working out basic addition, subtraction, multiplication, and division calculations.

This book has been carefully designed to guide you through some of the most useful mathematical techniques. Within this guide, you will be taught the following:

- Different tips and tricks to speedy maths!

- Learn the basics with regards to multiplication, division, addition, and subtraction.

- Sample questions, real-life challenges, and practice questions.

This pocketbook covers time-saving tips and tricks for improving your speed in mathematical calculations. Are you ready to challenge your mathematical knowledge?

Lets Get Started!

Before you continue, let us familiarise ourselves with some of the most common mathematical concepts that you SHOULD know!

Once you've taken a look over these concepts, then you can begin practising some of the best tips and tricks for acing your maths!

SYMBOLS

+	-	x	÷	=	n^2	≈
'plus' or 'add'	'subtract' or 'minus'	'times' or 'multiply'	'divided by'	'equals'	'a number squared'	'approximately equals'

ADDITION AND SUBTRACTION

+	1	2	3	4	5	6	7	8	9	10	11	12
1	2	3	4	5	6	7	8	9	10	11	12	13
2	3	4	5	6	7	8	9	10	11	12	13	14
3	4	5	6	7	8	9	10	11	12	13	14	15
4	5	6	7	8	9	10	11	12	13	14	15	16
5	6	7	8	9	10	11	12	13	14	15	16	17
6	7	8	9	10	11	12	13	14	15	16	17	18
7	8	9	10	11	12	13	14	15	16	17	18	19
8	9	10	11	12	13	14	15	16	17	18	19	20
9	10	11	12	13	14	15	16	17	18	19	20	21
10	11	12	13	14	15	16	17	18	19	20	21	22
11	12	13	14	15	16	17	18	19	20	21	22	23
12	13	14	15	16	17	18	19	20	21	22	23	24

MULTIPLICATION AND DIVISION

x	1	2	3	4	5	6	7	8	9	10	11	12
1	1	2	3	4	5	6	7	8	9	10	11	12
2	2	4	6	8	10	12	14	16	18	20	22	24
3	3	6	9	12	15	18	21	24	27	30	33	36
4	4	8	12	16	20	24	28	32	36	40	44	48
5	5	10	15	20	25	30	35	40	45	50	55	60
6	6	12	18	24	30	36	42	48	54	60	66	72
7	7	14	21	28	35	42	49	56	63	70	77	84
8	8	16	24	32	40	48	56	64	72	80	88	96
9	9	18	27	36	45	54	63	72	81	90	99	108
10	10	20	30	40	50	60	70	80	90	100	110	120
11	11	22	33	44	55	66	77	88	99	110	121	132
12	12	24	36	48	60	72	84	96	108	120	132	144

SQUARE NUMBERS

$1^2 = 1$	$2^2 = 4$	$3^2 = 9$	$4^2 = 16$
$5^2 = 25$	$6^2 = 36$	$7^2 = 49$	$8^2 = 64$
$9^2 = 81$	$10^2 = 100$	$11^2 = 121$	$12^2 = 144$
$13^2 = 169$	$14^2 = 196$	$15^2 = 225$	$16^2 = 256$
$17^2 = 289$	$18^2 = 324$	$19^2 = 361$	$20^2 = 400$

FRACTIONS, DECIMALS AND PERCENTAGES

$1/10 = 0.1 = 10\%$	$1/5 = 0.2 = 20\%$	$1/4 = 0.25 = 25\%$	$3/10 = 0.3 = 30\%$
$1/2 = 0.5 = 50\%$	$3/5 = 0.6 = 60\%$	$3/4 = 0.75 = 75\%$	$9/10 = 0.9 = 90\%$
$7/8 = 0.875 = 87 1/2 \%$	$5/8 = 0.625 - 62 1/2 \%$	$1/8 = 0.125 = 12 1/2\%$	$n/n = 1.0 = 100\%$

ADDITION AND SUBTRACTION
TIPS AND TRICKS

ADDING BY ALTERING

The theory for this trick uses multiples of 10 to make the calculation easier to answer. For example, you can alter the number by rounding the number up or down.

Example 1
64 + 48
Step 1 = Add 2 to the 48 to make 50
Step 2 = 64 + 50 = 114
Step 3 = Now minus the 2 that you added:
114 − 2 = 112

Answer = 112

Example 2
375 + 129
Step 1 = Add 1 to the 129 to make 130
Step 2 = 375 + 130 = 505
Step 3 = Now minus the 1 that you added
505 − 1 = 504

Answer = 504

ADDING BY GROUPING

When adding more than one-digit numbers, it is easier to GROUP the numbers in combinations.

Example 1

$4 + 6 + 3 + 1 + 6$

Step 1 = Look at the 4 and 6 and think 10

Step 2 = See the 3 and 1 and 6 and think 10

Step 3 = 10 + 10 = 20

Answer = 20

Example 2

$9 + 9 + 4 + 5 + 3 + 8 + 7 + 5$

Step 1 = Look at the 9 and the 9 and think 18

Step 2 = Look at the 5 and the 5 and think 10

Step 3 = Look at the 3 and the 7 and think 10

Step 4 = Look at the 4 and the 8 and think 12

Step 5 = 18 + 10 + 10 + 12 = 50

Answer = 50

ADDING WITHOUT CARRYING

Lots of addition calculations require you to carry numbers from one column over to another. Sometimes this causes small errors, resulting in an incorrect answer. The following trick allows you to work out the calculation WITHOUT having to carry numbers over.

Example 1

```
    75
    69
    25
    36
+   45
_____

    30   (Units column total)
    22   (Tens column total)
_____
   250
```

Example 2

```
   486
   369
   501
   222
+  600
_____

    18   (Units column total)
    16   (Tens column total)
    20   (Hundreds column total)
_____
  2178
```

The important thing to remember with this trick is how you line up the answers to each subtotal. Each subtotal is moved one column to the left of the previous one.

SUBTRACTING BY ADDING

You can subtract any number without even having to subtract any numbers at all. Sounds weird, doesn't it? But it can be done!

Example 1

Let's use the following: 465 - 58

Start by making both numbers the same length. This can be done by putting a 0 in front of the shorter one.

- 426 – 58 becomes 426 – 058

Now make the 3 digits on the bottom add up to 9 by adding the necessary amount:

- Add 9 to 0 to make it 9
- Add 4 to 5 to make it 9
- Add 1 to 8 to make it 9

Now the sum is:

426
- 941

Change the minus to an add:

426
+ 941
1367

SUBTRACTING IN TWO STEPS

Subtract the tens digits, and then the units. Let's take a look at a couple of examples.

Example 1

90 - 43

Step 1 = Ignore the 3 and think 90 – 40 = 50

Step 2 = Subtract the 3: 50 – 3 = 47

Answer = 47

Example 2

147 - 68

Step 1 = Ignore the 8 and think 147 – 60 = 87

Step 2 = Subtract the 8: 87 – 8 = 79

Answer = 79

ADDING FRACTIONS

There are several ways of adding fractions but they can be confusing and difficult to remember. Here is a way that uses a special name to help you remember it.

This is called the CROSSBOW METHOD.

Example 1

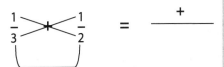

=

$$\frac{ + }{}$$

> We know the answer will be a fraction so we have drawn the line ready to receive the answer.
> It is an **add** sum, so we have put the + in.

The CROSS looks like a multiplication sign and it tells you which numbers to multiply together.

- One arm is saying 'multiply the 1 by the 2' and the other arm is saying 'multiply the 3 by the 1'.

The answer to 1 times 2 is 2. The answer to 3 times 1 is 3.

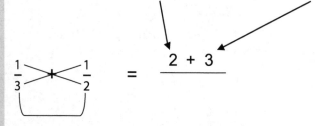

$$\frac{1}{3} \times \frac{1}{2} = \frac{2 + 3}{}$$

- The BOW says 'multiply the 3 by the 2'.

The answer is 6 and it goes underneath the line in the answer.

$$\frac{1}{3} \times \frac{1}{2} = \frac{2 + 3}{6}$$

> The **BOW** looks like a **U** (for underneath) and it is a reminder to put the answer underneath the line.

Finally, add up the numbers above the line.

$$\frac{1}{3} \diagdown\!\!\!\!+\!\!\!\!\diagup \frac{1}{2} = \frac{5}{6}$$

SUBTRACTING FRACTIONS

This is exactly the same method as adding fractions, but instead of adding the two top numbers, you will subtract them.

Example 1

$$\frac{1}{3} \diagdown\!\!\!\!\diagup \frac{2}{7} = \frac{7 - 6}{21}$$

ADDITION AND SUBTRACTION EXERCISES

Use the techniques taught in this chapter to work out the following calculations.

a) 86 + 54 =	h) 799 - 39 =
b) 468 + 896 =	i) 1,987 - 746 =
c) 83 + 48 + 32 + 10 + 8 =	j) 505 - 45 =
d) 4,036 + 4,068 + 3,987 =	k) 300 - 238 =
e) 4 + 4 + 2 + 6 + 4 + 12 =	l) 100 - 48 =
f) 89 + 42 + 36 + 49 + 47 + 36 =	m) 1,500 - 468 =
g) 1 + 1 + 1 + 6 + 8 + 2 + 6 =	n) 5,036 - 987 =

FRACTIONS EXERCISES

$\dfrac{1}{4} \times 24 = \dfrac{\square}{\square}$

$\dfrac{5}{8} \times 32 = \dfrac{\square}{\square}$

$\dfrac{5}{8} + \dfrac{3}{4} = \dfrac{\square}{\square}$

$\dfrac{5}{9} - \dfrac{3}{9} = \dfrac{\square}{\square}$

$\dfrac{2}{6} + \dfrac{2}{3} = \dfrac{\square}{\square}$

$\dfrac{3}{4} - \dfrac{1}{2} = \dfrac{\square}{\square}$

$\dfrac{5}{13} - \dfrac{4}{13} = \dfrac{\square}{\square}$

$\dfrac{6}{11} + \dfrac{4}{13} = \dfrac{\square}{\square}$

$2\dfrac{5}{6} + \dfrac{2}{4} = \dfrac{\square}{\square}$

$\dfrac{2}{7} + \dfrac{9}{10} = \dfrac{\square}{\square}$

$\dfrac{8}{11} - \dfrac{2}{4} = \dfrac{\square}{\square}$

$\dfrac{7}{12} + 1\dfrac{3}{7} = \dfrac{\square}{\square}$

MULTIPLICATION

TIPS AND TRICKS

In this chapter, you will learn different methods of doing different multiplication calculations.

Whether you are learning this from scratch, or simply refreshing your existing knowledge, this chapter will undoubtedly allow you to become competent with any multiplication question.

MULTIPLICATION OF WHOLE NUMBERS

Nearly everybody makes the same mistake with long multiplication. They manage the multiplication correctly but they get the answers in the wrong column. Here is a way of doing it that helps you get the answers in the correct column.

Example 1
251 x 47

251
47

To find the starting place when multiplying by 7, draw an arrow down through the first column. Draw another arrow where the answer will go. Where the arrows cross is the **starting** place. The answer starts at the starting place.

Multiply the top line by 7.

251
47
1757

NOTE that the answer starts in the starting place and then moves left.

To multiply by 4, we need to find the new starting place.

251
47
1757

To find the starting place when multiplying by 4. Draw an arrow down through the **second** column. Draw another arrow where the answer will go. Where the arrows cross is the **starting** place. The answer starts at the starting place.

Now multiply the top line by 4, and put the first answer in the starting place.

251
47
1757
1004

NOTE that the answer starts in the starting place (under the 5) and then moves left.

Now just add up the two rows in the answer to get the final answer.

MULTIPLICATION

33

```
  251
   47
 1757
1004
11797
```

MULTIPLICATION WITH ZEROES

Multiplication with zeroes is so simple! The best way to demonstrate this is via examples.

Example 1

50 x 40

Step 1 = Disregard the zeroes and think 5 x 4 = 20

Step 2 = Because two zeroes were included in the question, two zeroes need to be included in the answer.

Answer = 2,000

Example 2

400 x 30

Step 1 = Disregard the zeroes and think 4 x 3 = 12

Step 2 = Because three zeroes were included in the question, three zeroes need to be included in the answer.

Answer = 12,000

MULTIPLICATION WITH DECIMALS

The trick to multiplying numbers with decimals is to disregard the decimals, do the sum, and then put the decimals back in.

Example 1
2.34 x 1.7

```
  234
   17
 1638
  234
 3978
```

That's the answer, EXCEPT for the decimal point.

Count how many digits (numbers) were after the decimal point in the question.

2.34   1.7
one, two three

There are 3 digits after the decimal points in the question, so there must be 3 in the answer. 3978 becomes 3.978

3 digits after the decimal point, so we have finished!
2.34 x 1.7 = 3.978

MULTIPLICATION BY 5

The key to this technique is to divide the number by 2 and then insert any necessary zeroes.

Example 1

42 x 5

Step 1 = Divide: 42 ÷ 2 = 21

Step 2 = A rough estimate means that this is too small to be the correct answer. A quick estimate puts the answer somewhere in the 200s.

Step 3 = Affix one zero, which gives the answer 210

Answer = 210

Example 2

54.2 x 5

Step 1 = Disregard the decimal and think 542 x 5

Step 2 = Divide: 542 ÷ 2 = 271

Step 3 = 271 seems reasonable and is in fact the correct answer.

Answer = 271

MULTIPLICATION BY 11

The key to this technique is to write the number, leaving some space in the middle of the numbers. You will then need to add those numbers and the total should be placed in the middle of those two numbers.

Example 1
52 x 11
Step 1 = 5 _ 2
Step 2 = 5 + 2 = 7
Step 3 = Place the number 7 in the middle of these two numbers.

Answer = 572

Example 2
63 x 110
Step 1 = Disregard the zero and think 63 x 11
Step 2 = 6 _ 3
Step 3 = 6 + 3 = 9
Step 4 = Place the number 9 in the middle of these two numbers, and add the zero back in.

Answer = 6,930

MULTIPLICATION BY 9

The trick to multiplying any number by 9 is the following: Multiply the number (that's not 9) by 10. Using your answer to this calculation, subtract the original number to reach the correct answer.

Example 1
18 x 9
Step 1 = Multiply: 18 x 10 = 180
Step 2 = Subtract the original number: 180 – 18 = 162

Answer = 162

Example 2
450 x 9
Step 1 = Multiply: 450 x 10 = 4,500
Step 2 = Subtract the original number: 4,500 – 450 = 4,050

Answer = 4,050

MULTIPLICATION BY 25

The trick to multiplying any number by 25 is to divide the number by 4, and then using a rough guideline, add any zeroes to make the calculation correct.

Example 1
32 x 25

Step 1 = Divide: 32 ÷ 4 = 8

Step 2 = We know that roughly our answer should be somewhere in the 800s.

Step 3 = So we need to add two zeroes to 8 to get 800, and this is our answer.

Answer = 800

Example 2
138 x 25

Step 1 = Divide: 138 ÷ 4 = 34.5

Step 2 = We know that roughly our answer should be somewhere in the 3,000s.

Step 3 = So we need to move the decimal point two spaces to the right to get the answer of 3,450

Answer = 3,450

MULTIPLICATION

MULTIPLICATION BY 101

The trick to multiplying any number by 101 is the following: For one-digit numbers, write down the number twice and add a zero in the middle. For two-digit numbers, write down the number twice and you have your answer.

Example 1
38 x 101
Step 1 = Write down the number 38 twice: 3,838

Answer = 3,838

Example 2
8 x 101
Step 1 = Write down the number 8 twice: 88
Step 2 = Now add a zero in the middle: 808

Answer = 808

MULTIPLICATION BY 12

The key to multiplying a number by 12, is to first multiply the number by 10. Following this, you need to add two-times the original number.

Example 1
38 x 12
Step 1 = Multiply: 38 x 10 = 380
Step 2 = Work out twice the number: 38 x 2 = 76
Step 3 = 380 + 76 = 456

Answer = 456

Example 2
405 x 12
Step 1 = Multiply: 405 x 10 = 4,050
Step 2 = Work out twice the number: 405 x 2 = 810
Step 3 = 4,050 + 810 = 4,860

Answer = 4,860

MULTIPLICATION OF TWO-DIGIT NUMBERS

The trick to multiplying any two digit numbers is to multiply the ones digits together, then 'cross-multiply', and then finally multiply the tens digits.

Example 1

13 x 12

Step 1 = Multiply the ones digit: 3 x 2 = 6

Step 2 = Cross multiply and add: (1 x 2) + (3 x 1) = 5

Step 3 = Multiply the tens digit: 1 x 1 = 1

Answer = 156

Example 2

23 x 11

Step 1 = Multiply the ones digit: 3 x 1 = 3

Step 2 = Cross multiply and add: (2 x 1) + (3 x 1) = 5

Step 3 = Multiply the tens digit: 2 x 1 = 2

Answer = 253

MULTIPLICATION IN TWO STEPS

The trick to multiplying in two easy steps is simple: divide one number into two smaller ones to make the calculation more manageable.

Example 1
8 x 16

Step 1 = Split 16 into two parts: 8 x 2

Step 2 = Now work out the following: 8 x 8 x 2

Step 3 = (8 x 8) x 2

Step 4 = 64 x 2 = 128

Answer = 128

Example 2
18 x 320

Step 1 = Disregard the zero and think: 18 x 32

Step 2 = Split 32 into two parts: 16 x 2

Step 3 = Now work out the following: 18 x 16 x 2

Step 4 = (18 x 16) x 2

Step 5 = 288 x 2 = 576

Step 6 = Now add the zero back on.

Answer = 5,760

MULTIPLICATION BY REGROUPING

The key to multiplying by regrouping is to group numbers so that it is easier to manage.

Example 1
16 x 14
Step 1 = Regroup: (14 x 14) + (14 x 2)
Step 2 = 196 + 28 = 224

Answer = 224

Example 2
606 x 6
Step 1 = Regroup: (600 x 6) + (6 x 6)
Step 2 = 3,600 + 36 = 3,636

Answer = 3,636

MULTIPLICATION OF FRACTIONS

Once again there is a special name to help you to remember how to multiply fractions. It is called the ARROW METHOD. Here's how it works.

Example 1

To multiply $\frac{2}{3}$ by $\frac{3}{4}$, you need to write out the sum.

$\frac{2}{3} \times \frac{3}{4} = $ —— and put the line ready for the answer.

Now put the arrows in.

$$\frac{2}{3} \times \frac{3}{4} = \text{——}$$

Now multiply the numbers that the arrows touch; and put the answers above and underneath the answer line.

$$\frac{2}{3} \times \frac{3}{4} = \frac{6}{12}$$ This can also be simplified to $^1/_2$!

GRID MULTIPLICATION

One of the easiest ways of multiplying any number is to use the grid method.

Example 1

Work out 456 x 17

Step 1 = 400 (hundreds)

50 (tens)

6 (units)

x	400	50	6
10			
7			

x	400	50	6
10	4,000	500	60
7	2,800	350	42

Step 2 = 10 (tens)

7 (units)

x	400	50	6	TOTAL
10	4,000	500	60	**4,560**
7	2,800	350	42	**3,192**

Step 3 = Multiply all of the columns by the rows.

Step 4 = Working along each row, add up the totals. 4,560 + 3,192 = 7,752

Answer = 7,752

MULTIPLICATION EXERCISES

Use the techniques taught in this chapter to work out the following calculations.

a) 18 x 19 =	h) 89 x 500 =
b) 500 x 9 =	i) 789 x 11 =
c) 4.23 x 1.8 =	j) 48 x 110 =
d) 3.25 x 24 =	k) 78 x 25 =
e) 6.5 x 1,000 =	l) 400 x 101 =
f) 900 x 300 =	m) 987 x 12 =
g) 79.5 x 5 =	n) 7,820 x 6 =

$2\frac{4}{5} \times 15 = \dfrac{\square}{\square}$ $1\frac{1}{4} \times 48 = \dfrac{\square}{\square}$

$\dfrac{3}{8} \times \dfrac{11}{14} = \dfrac{\square}{\square}$ $\dfrac{1}{2} \times \dfrac{3}{4} = \dfrac{\square}{\square}$ $\dfrac{7}{11} \times \dfrac{3}{8} = \dfrac{\square}{\square}$ $\dfrac{2}{3} \times \dfrac{6}{7} = \dfrac{\square}{\square}$

$\dfrac{1}{12} \times \dfrac{1}{6} = \dfrac{\square}{\square}$ $\dfrac{1}{3} \times 21 = \dfrac{\square}{\square}$

DIVISION
TIPS AND TRICKS

In this chapter, you will learn different methods of doing different division calculations.

Whether you are learning this from scratch, or simply refreshing your existing knowledge, this chapter will undoubtedly allow you to become competent with any division question.

DIVISION OF WHOLE NUMBERS

Division of whole numbers is relatively simple as long as you follow a few simple rules and keep everything neat and tidy.

Example 1

$195 \div 15$

We are dividing by 15, so let's write down the times table for 15.
You will see why in a minute.

| 15 | 30 | 45 | 60 | 75 | 90 | 105 | 120 | 135 |

It's quite easy to do that because you just start with 15 and then keep adding 15 until you have 9 answers.

Now for the sum.

$$15) \overline{195}$$

15 into 1 won't go (it goes 0 times). So put a 0 above the 1.

$$\frac{0}{15)195}$$

The answer always goes above the number we have reached, and at the moment we have only reached the first number (1).

So we proceed to the second number.

$$\frac{0}{15)195}$$

15 into 19 goes 1 time. Put a '1' above the number we have reached (9).

$$\frac{01}{15)195}$$
$$15$$

Write the 15 **neatly** under the sum and subtract to find the remainder.

```
   01
15)195
   15        19 – 15 = 4
    4
```

Now we have dealt with the 1 and the 9 but not the 5.
Put the 5 next to the remainder.

```
   01
15)195
   15
   45
```

Now it's a case of 15 into 45 and this is why we wrote down the times table for
15. Look at the times table above and you will see that 3 x 15 comes to 45 exactly.
Put the answer exactly above the 5 in the original sum, because we move along
the sum one number at a time.

```
    013
15) 195
    15
    45
    45
    00
```

3 x 15 = 45 so write it down and subtract to find the remainder.

There isn't a remainder so the sum is finished.

195 ÷ 15 = 013 which is 13 because the 0 at the front only means that there are 0 hundreds.

Answer = 13

DIVISION WITH DECIMALS

The trick to dividing numbers with decimals is to disregard the decimals, do the sum, and then put the decimals back in.

Example 1

$72 \div 3.6$

Step 1 = Disregard the zeroes: $72 \div 36$

Step 2 = $72 \div 36 = 2$

Step 3 = There was one number after the decimal point, so one number has to come after the decimal point in the answer.

Answer = 20

Example 2

$147 \div 4.9$

Step 1 = Disregard the zeroes: $147 \div 49$

Step 2 = $147 \div 49 = 3$

Step 3 = There was one number after the decimal point, so one number has to come after the decimal point in the answer.

Answer = 30

DIVISION BY 5, 50, 500 AND SO ON...

The trick to dividing any number 5 is the following: Multiply the number by 2, and affix any necessary zeroes or decimal points, based on your guesstimation.

Example 1

$265 \div 5$

Step 1 = Multiply 265 x 2 = 530

Step 2 = You know that our answer should be somewhere in the 50s.

Step 3 = That means if we get rid of the zero, we would have 53

Answer = 53

Example 2

$122 \div 5$

Step 1 = Multiply 122 x 2 = 244

Step 2 = You know that our answer should be somewhere in the 20s.

Step 3 = That means we can move the decimal point one space to the left, and we get 24.4

Answer = 24.4

DIVISION BY 25, 2.5, 250 AND SO ON...

The trick to dividing any number by 25 is the following: Multiply the number by 4 and then affix any zeroes or decimal points where necessary.

Example 1

600 ÷ 25

Step 1 = Disregard the zeroes and then multiply by 4: 6 x 4 = 24

Step 2 = Using a rough estimate, you know that our answer should be somewhere in the 20s.

Step 3 = Therefore, 24 would be our answer.

Answer = 24

Example 2

900 ÷ 2.5

Step 1 = Disregard the zeroes and then multiply by 4: 9 x 4 = 36

Step 2 = A quick estimate would mean that our answer should be somewhere in the 300s. So, we need to add a zero.

Answer = 360

DIVISION BY 125, 1.25, 12.5, 1,250 AND SO ON...

The trick to dividing by 125 is the following: Multiply the number by 8 and then affix any zeroes or decimal points where neccessary.

Example 1

900 ÷ 125

Step 1 = Disregard the zeroes and think 9 x 8 = 72

Step 2 = You know that our answer should be somewhere in the tens. So, we need to add a decimal point in.

Step 3 = That means our answer would become 7.2

Answer = 7.2

Example 2

5,000 ÷ 12.5

Step 1 = Disregard the zeroes and think 5 x 8 = 40

Step 2 = You know that our answer should be somewhere in the 400s.

Step 3 = That means we can add one zero to 40 which becomes 400

Answer = 400

DIVISION BY NUMBERS ENDING IN 9

The trick to dividing any number that ends in 9 is relatively straightforward. You will need to think 'repetition' with regards to this division trick. Let us show you with a couple of examples.

Example 1
$8 \div 9 = 0.888888...$

Example 2
$52 \div 99 = 0.525252...$

Example 3
$304 \div 999 = 0.304304...$

Example 4
$200 \div 99 = 2.020202...$

DIVISION BY 4, 40, 400 AND SO ON...

The trick to dividing by 4 is the following: Halve the number, and then halve again.

Example 1

$284 \div 4$

Step 1 = Halve the number: $284 \div 2 = 124$

Step 2 = Now halve the number again: $124 \div 2 = 62$

Answer = 62

Example 2

$1,880 \div 40$

Step 1 = Have the number: $1,880 \div 2 = 940$

Step 2 = Now halve the number again: $940 \div 2 = 470$

Answer = 470

DIVISION OF FRACTIONS

Once again there is a special name to help you to remember how to divide fractions. It uses the same method as multiplying fractions – **ARROW METHOD**. The biggest difference is to ALWAYS remember to turn the second fraction **UPSIDE DOWN** and change the **DIVIDE SIGN TO A MULTIPLICATION SIGN**. Here's how it works.

Example 1

$$\frac{2}{3} \div \frac{4}{5} = \underline{\hspace{2cm}}$$

Last fraction turned upside down and ÷ changed to x

$$\frac{2}{3} \times \frac{5}{4} = \underline{\hspace{2cm}}$$

Now multiply.

$\dfrac{2}{3} \times \dfrac{5}{4} = \dfrac{10}{12}$ That is the answer...but it simplifies to $\dfrac{5}{6}$.

Easy. $\dfrac{5}{6}$ is the answer to the original divide sum.

DIVISION EXERCISES

Use the techniques taught in this chapter to work out the following calculations.

a) $37.5 \div 7.5 =$	h) $4,800 \div 40 =$
b) $985 \div 5 =$	i) $60 \div 3 =$
c) $50,000 \div 0.5 =$	j) $50.5 \div 0.5 =$
d) $6,250 \div 250 =$	k) $5,700 \div 150 =$
e) $750 \div 12.5 =$	l) $120 \div 1.5 =$
f) $6 \div 9 =$	m) $475 \div 95 =$
g) $300 \div 99 =$	n) $222 \div 25 =$

$\dfrac{1}{2} \div 4 = \dfrac{\square}{\square}$ $\dfrac{2}{8} \div 2 = \dfrac{\square}{\square}$

$\dfrac{3}{9} \div \dfrac{1}{3} = \dfrac{\square}{\square}$ $\dfrac{3}{5} \div 6 = \dfrac{\square}{\square}$

$\dfrac{3}{100} \div 10 = \dfrac{\square}{\square}$ $\dfrac{7}{10} \div 10 = \dfrac{\square}{\square}$

SQUARED NUMBERS

NUMBERS

TIPS AND TRICKS

In this chapter, we are going to take a look at a couple of tips and tricks for dealing with squared numbers.

SQUARING A NUMBER ENDING IN 1

When it comes to squared numbers, the best way to solve the calculation is to break it down. Take a look at the following examples to see this neat little trick!

Example 1

11^2

Step 1 = Square: $10^2 = 10 \times 10 = 100$

Step 2 = Add: $10 + 11 = 21$

Step 3 = $100 + 21 = 121$

Answer = 121

Example 2

91^2

Step 1 = Square: $90^2 = 90 \times 90 = 8,100$

Step 2 = Add: $90 + 91 = 181$

Step 3 = $8,100 + 181 = 8,281$

Answer = 8,281

SQUARING A TWO-DIGIT NUMBER BEGINNING WITH 5

When it comes to squaring numbers, this is also another handy trick to learn. This trick will work for ANY number beginning with 5. The technique is as follows: add 25 to the units digits. Using the units number, affix the square to it.

The key thing to remember is the following:
5 x 5 = 25

Example 1
53^2
Step 1 = Add: 25 + 3 = 28
Step 2 = 3^2 = 3 x 3 = 9 (09)
Step 3 = Combine the numbers: 2,809

Answer = 2,809

Example 2
58^2
Step 1 = Add: 25 + 8 = 33
Step 2 = 8^2 = 8 x 8 = 64
Step 3 = Combine the numbers: 3,364

Answer = 3,364

SQUARING ANY TWO-DIGIT NUMBER

There is a simple trick to remember which will allow you to calculate the square numbers of any two-digit number.

Example 1

32^2

Step 1 = Find the distance between the tens and the units. Distance between 30 and 32 is 2

Step 2 = 32 − 2 = 30

Step 3 = 30 + 2 + 2 = 34

Step 4 = 30 x 34 = 1,020

Step 5 = Multiply the distance number by itself: 2 x 2 = 4

Step 6 = 1,020 + 4 = 1,024

Answer = 1,024

Example 2

64^2

Step 1 = Find the distance between the tens and the units. Distance between 60 and 64 is 4

Step 2 = 64 − 4 = 60

Step 3 = 64 + 4 = 68

Step 4 = 60 x 68 = 4,080

Step 5 = Multiply the distance number by itself: 4 x 4 = 16

Step 6 = 4,080 + 16 = 4,096

Answer = 4,096

SQUARED NUMBERS EXERCISES

Use the techniques taught in this chapter to work out the following calculations.

a) $91^2 =$	h) $9^2 =$
b) $51^2 =$	i) $304^2 =$
c) $56^2 =$	j) $32.1^2 =$
d) $506^2 =$	k) $570^2 =$
e) $5.2^2 =$	l) $62^2 =$
f) $18^2 =$	m) $101^2 =$
g) $142^2 =$	n) $500^2 =$

GUESSTIMATION

TIPS AND TRICKS

In this chapter, we are going to take a look at a couple of tips and tricks to calculate quick estimations.

ESTIMATION – MULTIPLICATION BY 33 OR 34

When it comes to estimating an answer with regards to multiplying by 33 or 34, you can divide the number by 3, and then affix any zeroes or decimal points if necessary.

Example 1
Estimate 42 x 33
Step 1 = Divide: 42 ÷ 3 = 14
Step 2 = A quick estimate should put the answer in the 1,000s. That means we need to add two zeroes.

Answer ≈ 1,400

Example 2
Estimate 96 x 34
Step 1 = Divide: 96 ÷ 3 = 32
Step 2 = A quick estimate should put the answer in the 3,000s. That means we need to add two zeroes.

Answer ≈ 3,200

The symbol for approximately is ≈.

ESTIMATION – MULTIPLICATION BY 49 OR 51

When it comes to estimating an answer with regards to multiplying by 49 or 51, you can divide the number by 2, and then affix any zeroes or decimal points if necessary.

Example 1
Estimate 64 x 51
Step 1 = Divide: 64 ÷ 2 = 32
Step 2 = A quick estimate should put the answer in the 3,000s. That means we need to add two zeroes.

Answer ≈ 3,200

Example 2
Estimate 49 x 82
Step 1 = Divide: 82 ÷ 2 = 41
Step 2 = A quick estimate should put the answer in the 4,000s. That means we need to add two zeroes.

Answer ≈ 4,100

ESTIMATION – MULTIPLICATION BY 66 OR 67

When it comes to estimating an answer with regards to multiplying by 66 or 67, you can multiply by $^2/_3$, and then affix any zeroes or decimal points if necessary.

Example 1

Estimate 67 x 30

Step 1 = Multiply: 30 x $^2/_3$ = 20

Step 2 = A quick estimate should put the answer in the 2,000s. That means we need to add two zeroes.

Answer ≈ 2,000

Example 2

Estimate 42 x 66

Step 1 = Multiply: 42 x $^2/_3$ = 28

Step 2 = A quick estimate should put the answer in the 2,000s. That means we need to add two zeroes.

Answer ≈ 2,800

ESTIMATION – DIVISION BY 33 OR 34

When it comes to estimating an answer with regards to dividing by 33 or 34, you can multiply the number by 3, and then affix any zeroes or decimal points if necessary.

Example 1
Estimate 408 ÷ 34
Step 1 = Multiply: 408 x 3 = 1,224
Step 2 = A quick estimate should put the answer in the 10s. That means we need to add a decimal point.

Answer ≈ 12.24

Example 2
Estimate 858 ÷ 33
Step 1 = Multiply: 858 x 3 = 2,574
Step 2 = A quick estimate should put the answer in the 20s. That means we need to add a decimal point.

Answer ≈ 25.74

ESTIMATION – DIVISION BY 49 OR 51

When it comes to estimating an answer with regards to dividing by 49 or 51, you can multiply the number by 2, and then affix any zeroes or decimal points if necessary.

Example 1

Estimate 784 ÷ 49

Step 1 = Multiply: 784 x 2 = 1,568

Step 2 = A quick estimate should put the answer in the 10s. That means we need to add a decimal point.

Answer ≈ 15.68

Example 2

Estimate 918 ÷ 51

Step 1 = Multiply: 918 x 2 = 1,836

Step 2 = A quick estimate should put the answer in the 10s. That means we need to add a decimal point.

Answer ≈ 18.36

ESTIMATION – DIVISION BY 66 OR 67

When it comes to estimating an answer with regards to dividing by 66 or 67, you can multiply the number by 1.5, and then affix any zeroes or decimal points if necessary.

Example 1
Estimate 1,716 ÷ 66
Step 1 = Multiply: 1,716 x 1.5 = 2,574
Step 2 = A quick estimate should put the answer in the 20s. That means we need to add a decimal point.

Answer ≈ 25.74

Example 2
Estimate 536 ÷ 67
Step 1 = Multiply: 536 x 1.5 = 804
Step 2 = A quick estimate should put the answer in the units. That means we need to add a decimal point.

Answer ≈ 8.04

ESTIMATION – DIVISION BY 9, 90, 900 AND SO ON...

When it comes to estimating an answer with regards to dividing by 9, you can multiply the number by 11, and then affix any zeroes or decimal points if necessary.

Example 1

Estimate 513 ÷ 9

Step 1 = Multiply: 513 x 11 = 5,643

Step 2 = A quick estimate should put the answer in the 50s. That means we need to add a decimal point.

Answer ≈ 56.43

Example 2

Estimate 1,260 ÷ 90

Step 1 = Multiply: 1,260 x 11 = 13,860

Step 2 = A quick estimate should put the answer in the 10s. That means we need to add a decimal point.

Answer ≈ 13.86

ESTIMATION – DIVISION BY 11, 1.1, 110 AND SO ON...

When it comes to estimating an answer with regards to dividing by 11, you can multiply the number by 9, and then affix any zeroes or decimal points if necessary.

Example 1
Estimate 250 ÷ 11
Step 1 = Multiply: 250 x 9 = 2,250
Step 2 = A quick estimate should put the answer in the 20s. That means we need to add a decimal point.

Answer ≈ 22.50

Example 2
Estimate 16 ÷ 1.1
Step 1 = Multiply: 16 x 9 = 144
Step 2 = A quick estimate should put the answer in the 10s. That means we need to add a decimal point.

Answer ≈ 14.4

ESTIMATION – DIVISION BY 14, 1.4, 140 AND SO ON...

When it comes to estimating an answer with regards to dividing by 14, you can multiply the number by 7, and then affix any zeroes or decimal points if necessary.

Example 1

Estimate 112 ÷ 1.4

Step 1 = Multiply: 112 x 7 = 784

Step 2 = A quick estimate should put the answer near the 80s. That means we need to add a decimal point.

Answer ≈ 78.4

Example 2

Estimate 406 ÷ 14

Step 1 = Multiply: 406 x 7 = 2,842

Step 2 = A quick estimate should put the answer in the 20s. That means we need to add a decimal point.

Answer ≈ 28.42

ESTIMATION – DIVISION BY 17. 1.7, 170 AND SO ON...

When it comes to estimating an answer with regards to dividing by 17, you can multiply the number by 6, and then affix any zeroes or decimal points if necessary.

Example 1

Estimate 1,751 ÷ 17

Step 1 = Multiply: 1,751 x 6 = 10,506

Step 2 = A quick estimate should put the answer in the 100s. That means we need to add a decimal point.

Answer ≈ 105.06

Example 2

Estimate 11 ÷ 1.7

Step 1 = Multiply: 11 x 6 = 66

Step 2 = A quick estimate should put the answer in the units. That means we need to add a decimal point.

Answer ≈ 6.6

GUESSTIMATION

GUESSTIMATION EXERCISES

Use the techniques taught in this chapter to work out estimates to the following calculations.

a) $3,000 \div 17 \approx$	h) $4,080 \div 51 \approx$
b) $640 \div 49 \approx$	i) $78 \times 49 \approx$
c) $66 \times 102 \approx$	j) $1,000 \div 14 \approx$
d) $800 \div 11 \approx$	k) $560 \div 17 \approx$
e) $900 \div 9 \approx$	l) $120 \div 9 \approx$
f) $49 \times 34 \approx$	m) $49 \times 12 \approx$
g) $33 \times 87 \approx$	n) $1,474 \div 67 \approx$

ANSWERS TO EXERCISES

ANSWERS TO ADDITION AND SUBTRACTION (PAGE 28)

a) 86 + 54 = 140

b) 468 + 896 = 1,364

c) 83 + 48 + 32 + 10 + 8 = 181

d) 4,036 + 4,068 + 3,987 = 12,091

e) 4 + 4 + 2 + 6 + 4 + 12 = 32

f) 89 + 42 + 36 + 49 + 47 + 36 = 299

g) 1 + 1 + 1 + 6 + 8 + 2 + 6 = 25

h) 799 - 39 = 760

i) 1,987 - 746 = 1,241

j) 505 - 45 = 460

k) 300 - 238 = 62

l) 100 - 48 = 52

m) 1,500 - 468 = 1,032

n) 5,036 - 987 = 4,049

$$\frac{2}{7} + \frac{3}{7} = \boxed{\frac{5}{7}}$$

$$\frac{8}{10} - \frac{1}{4} = \boxed{\frac{11}{20}}$$

$$\frac{5}{8} + \frac{3}{4} = \boxed{\frac{11}{8}}$$

$$\frac{5}{9} - \frac{3}{9} = \boxed{\frac{2}{9}}$$

$$\frac{2}{6} + \frac{2}{3} = \boxed{\frac{1}{1}}$$

$$\frac{3}{4} - \frac{1}{2} = \boxed{\frac{1}{4}}$$

$$\frac{5}{13} - \frac{4}{13} = \boxed{\frac{1}{13}}$$

$$\frac{6}{11} + \frac{4}{13} = \boxed{\frac{122}{143}}$$

$$2\frac{5}{6} + \frac{2}{4} = \boxed{\frac{80}{24}}$$

$$\frac{2}{7} + \frac{9}{10} = \boxed{\frac{83}{70}}$$

$$\frac{8}{11} - \frac{2}{4} = \boxed{\frac{5}{22}}$$

$$\frac{7}{12} + 1\frac{3}{7} = \boxed{\frac{169}{84}}$$

For the purpose of these tricks, we have not simplified our answers.

Rapid Maths Pocketbook

a) 18 x 19 = 342	h) 89 x 500 = 44,500
b) 500 x 9 = 4,500	i) 789 x 11 = 8,679
c) 4.23 x 1.8 = 7,614	j) 48 x 110 = 5,280
d) 3.25 x 24 = 78	k) 78 x 25 = 1,950
e) 6.5 x 1,000 = 6,500	l) 400 x 101 = 40,400
f) 900 x 300 = 270,000	m) 987 x 12 = 11,844
g) 79.5 x 5 = 397.5	n) 7,820 x 6 = 46,920

$$2\frac{4}{5} \times 15 = \frac{42}{1}$$

$$1\frac{1}{4} \times 48 = \frac{60}{1}$$

$$\frac{1}{12} \times \frac{1}{6} = \frac{1}{72}$$

$$\frac{1}{3} \times 21 = \frac{21}{3}$$

$$\frac{3}{8} \times \frac{11}{14} = \frac{33}{112}$$

$$\frac{1}{2} \times \frac{3}{4} = \frac{3}{8}$$

$$\frac{7}{11} \times \frac{3}{8} = \frac{21}{88}$$

$$\frac{2}{3} \times \frac{6}{7} = \frac{4}{7}$$

For the purpose of these tricks, we have not simplified our answers.

ANSWERS TO DIVISION (PAGE 62)

a) $37.5 \div 7.5 = 5$	h) $4,800 \div 40 = 120$
b) $985 \div 5 = 197$	i) $60 \div 3 = 20$
c) $50,000 \div 0.5 = 100,000$	j) $50.5 \div 0.5 = 101$
d) $6,250 \div 250 = 25$	k) $5,700 \div 150 = 38$
e) $750 \div 12.5 = 60$	l) $120 \div 1.5 = 80$
f) $6 \div 9 = 0.666666...$	m) $475 \div 95 = 5$
g) $300 \div 99 = 3.030303...$	n) $222 \div 25 = 8.88$

$\dfrac{1}{2} \div 4 = \dfrac{\boxed{1}}{\boxed{8}}$ $\dfrac{2}{8} \div 2 = \dfrac{\boxed{1}}{\boxed{8}}$ $\dfrac{3}{100} \div 10 = \dfrac{\boxed{3}}{\boxed{1000}}$ $\dfrac{7}{10} \div 10 = \dfrac{\boxed{7}}{\boxed{100}}$

$\dfrac{3}{9} \div \dfrac{1}{3} = \dfrac{\boxed{1}}{\boxed{1}}$ $\dfrac{3}{5} \div 6 = \dfrac{\boxed{1}}{\boxed{10}}$

ANSWERS TO SQUARED NUMBERS (PAGE 69)

a) $91^2 = 8,281$	h) $9^2 = 81$
b) $51^2 = 2,601$	i) $304^2 = 92,416$
c) $56^2 = 3,136$	j) $32.1^2 = 1,030.41$
d) $506^2 = 256,036$	k) $570^2 = 324,900$
e) $5.2^2 = 27.04$	l) $62^2 = 3,844$
f) $18^2 = 324$	m) $101^2 = 10,201$
g) $142^2 = 20,164$	n) $500^2 = 250,000$

ANSWERS TO GUESSTIMATION (PAGE 82)

a) $3,000 \div 17 \approx 180$

b) $640 \div 49 \approx 12.80$

c) $66 \times 102 \approx 6,800$

d) $800 \div 11 \approx 72.0$

e) $900 \div 9 \approx 100$

f) $49 \times 34 \approx 16.66$

g) $33 \times 87 \approx 287.1$

h) $4,080 \div 51 \approx 81.60$

i) $78 \times 49 \approx 3,900$

j) $1,000 \div 14 \approx 70.0$

k) $560 \div 17 \approx 33.6$

l) $120 \div 9 \approx 13.20$

m) $49 \times 12 \approx 58.8$

n) $1,474 \div 67 \approx 22.11$

PUT YOUR KNOWLEDGE TO THE TEST

In this chapter, we thought it would be a good idea to share with you some sample mathematical questions. Our advice is to practice these questions, using the methods and tricks that we have taught you throughout this guide.

This chapter will use all the content from the previous chapters, including:
- Addition;
- Subtraction;
- Multiplication;
- Division;
- Squared Numbers;
- Guesstimation.

 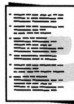

Work through the following questions, and then check your answer in the next chapter!

Good luck!

Question 1

a)

0.45 + 0.983

----

b)

0.35 + 2.68

----

c)

5.68 – 2.47

----

d)

3.5 x 6.2

Question 2

Complete the following sums:

a) $3^2 + 5^2 =$ _____

b) $4^2 + 3^2 =$ _____

c) $5^2 - 2^2 =$ _____

d) $7^2 - 5^2 =$ _____

e) $4^2 \times 2^2 =$ _____

f) $4^2 \div 2^2 =$ _____

g) $3^3 + 2^3 =$ _____

h) $4^3 - 3^3 =$ _____

Question 3

Fill in the missing blanks.

Square Number $\boxed{}$ + Square Number $\boxed{}$ = 52

Question 4

Complete the following sums:

a)
```
  21947
-   906
_____
```

b)
```
   968
+  366
_____
```

c)
```
8 ) 940
```

d)
```
    395
X     6
_____
```

Question 5

Work out the calculation:

a)
```
    896
    425
     23
+   129
_____
```

b)
```
    965
    236
     48
-    36
_____
```

c)
```
    876
     23
     91
-    40
_____
```

d)
```
   54236
    5614
      87
+      9
_____
```

Question 6

Complete the following sums:

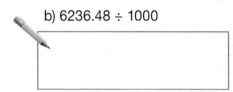

a) 458 x 10

b) 6236.48 ÷ 1000

Question 7

Complete the following sums:

a)

```
    5 3 6
x       8
_____
```

b)

```
  1 4 6 8
x       4
_____
```

c)

```
    3 9 8
x       5
_____
```

d)

```
  1 2 3 4
x       6
_____
```

Question 8

Work out the following:

a) 8^2 _____

b) 4^3 _____

c) 11^2 _____

d) 5^3 _____

Question 9

Fill in the missing blanks:

a) $1000 \times \boxed{} = 3125$

b) $\boxed{} \times 100 = 3.216$

c) $32.568 \div \boxed{} = 3.2568$

d) $\boxed{} \div 100 = 9.6312$

Question 10

Work out the calculation:

X	300		2
20	6,000	1,400	
5		350	

Question 11

Lola spends £1,456.80 in 20 days. How much does Lola spend per day?

Question 12

Work out the following sums.

a)
```
   £  6.85
 + £  4.68
_____

_____
```

b)
```
   £ 13.24
 + £ 25.63
_____

_____
```

c)
```
   £ 10.08
 - £  5.73
_____

_____
```

d)
```
   £ 182.54
 - £ 112.35
_____

_____
```

Question 13

A family of four spend £368.80 on their weekly food shopping. If the four members of the family split the cost equally, how much will each of them pay?

Question 14

Jason goes to the cinema with his friend Matt. Each of them buys a tub of popcorn. For 800 grams of popcorn, it costs £5.00. How much would 200 grams of popcorn cost?

Question 15

Work out the following sums:

a)
```
  £ 236.98
-
  £ 105.69
  _____


  _____
```

b)
```
  £ 789.42
+
  £ 245.53
  _____


  _____
```

c)
```
  £  86.23
+
  £   9.76
  _____


  _____
```

d)
```
  £ 468.74
+
  £  57.42
  _____


  _____
```

Question 16

Complete the table below by filling in the missing numbers.

x	x^2
4	16
_____	9
2	_____
10	_____

Question 17

Using the information that:

$$562 \times 68 = 38{,}216$$

Find the value of the following calculations:

a) 5.62 x 68 =

b) 5.62 x 6.8 =

c) 38,216 ÷ 6.8 =

d) 0.562 x 0.68 =

Question 18

7,890 x 32 =

Question 19

12 x 10 x 8 =

Question 20

Have a go at these quick-fire calculations:

a) 594 x 11	f) 21 x 13	k) 300 ÷ 125	p) 24 x 600
b) 40 x 66	g) 14 x 52	l) 12 x 14	q) 64 x 101
c) $6^2 - 4^2$	h) 1.8 x 120	m) 1.9 x 16	r) 44 x 87
d) 44 - 29	i) 1.8 x 1.3	n) 890 - 698	s) 5,352 - 201
e) 117 - 65	j) 1,110 ÷ 125	o) 3,600 ÷ 40	t) 118^2

PUT YOUR KNOWLEDGE TO THE TEST ANSWERS

Question 1
a) 1.433
b) 3.03
c) 3.21
d) 21.7

Question 2
a) 34
b) 25
c) 21
d) 24
e) 64
f) 4
g) 35
h) 37

Question 3
36 and 16

Question 4
a) 21,041
b) 1,334
c) 117.5
d) 2,370

Question 5
a) 1,473
b) 645
c) 722
d) 59,946

Question 6
a) 4,580
b) 6.23648

Question 7
a) 4,288
b) 5,872
c) 1,990
d) 7,404

Question 8
a) 64
b) 64
c) 121
d) 125

Question 9
a) 3.125
b) 0.03216
c) 10
d) 963.12

Question 10

x	300	70	2
20	6,000	1,400	40
5	1,500	350	10

Answer = 9,300

Question 11
72.84

Question 12
a) £11.53
b) £38.87
c) £4.35
d) £70.19

Question 13
£92.20

Question 14
£1.25

Question 15
a) £131.29
b) £1,034.95
c) £95.99
d) £526.16

Question 16

x	x^2
4	16
3	9
2	4
10	100

Question 17
a) 382.16
b) 38.216
c) 5,620
d) 0.38216

Question 18
252,480

Question 19
960

Question 20
a) 6,534
b) 2,640
c) 20
d) 15
e) 52
f) 273
g) 728
h) 216
i) 2.34

j) 8.8
k) 2.4
l) 168
m) 30.4
n) 192
o) 90
p) 14,400
q) 6,464
r) 3,828
s) 5,151
t) 13,924

CHECK OUT OUR OTHER POCKETBOOK GUIDES:

FOR MORE INFORMATION ON OUR REVISION GUIDES, PLEASE CHECK OUT THE FOLLOWING:

WWW.HOW2BECOME.COM

Get Access to

FREE Educational

Tests

www.MyEducationalTests.co.uk